GRADE **07**

PIANO

Pieces & Exercises for
Trinity College London
Exams 2018-2020

Includes CD &
teaching notes

Published by
Trinity College London Press
trinitycollege.com

Registered in England
Company no. 09726123

Copyright © 2017 Trinity College London Press
First impression, June 2017

Unauthorised photocopying is illegal
No part of this publication may be copied or reproduced in any
form or by any means without the prior permission of the publisher.

Printed in England by Halstan & Co Ltd., Amersham, Bucks

Allegro

from *Suite no. 7 in G minor*, HWV 432

George Frideric Handel
(1685-1759)

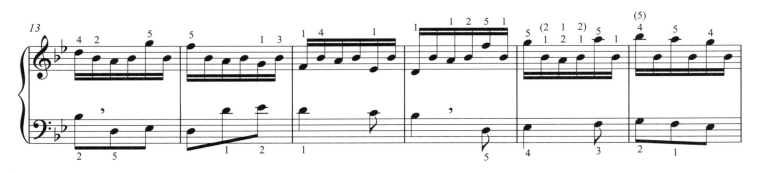

© Copyright 2017 Trinity College London Press

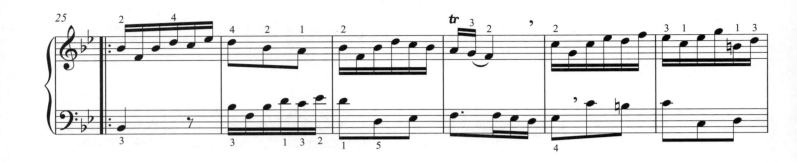

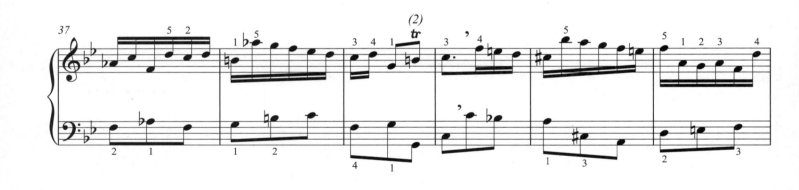

4

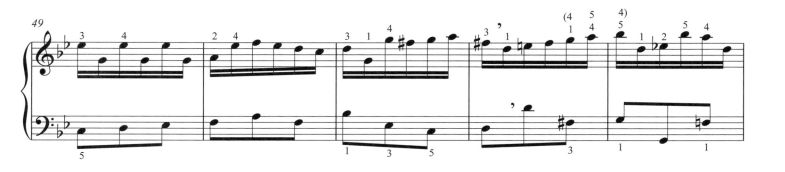

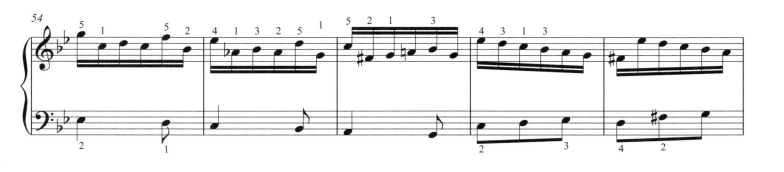

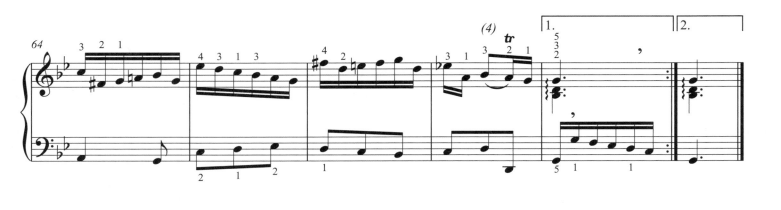

5

Minuet in D major

K. 355

Wolfgang Amadeus Mozart
(1756-1791)

© Copyright 2017 Trinity College London Press

Allegro

First movement from *Sonate*, op. 6

Anton Eberl
(1765–1807)

© Copyright 2017 Trinity College London Press

[Blank page to facilitate page turns]

Etude in A minor
op. 58 no. 6

Ed. Snell

Ludvig Schytte
(1848-1909)

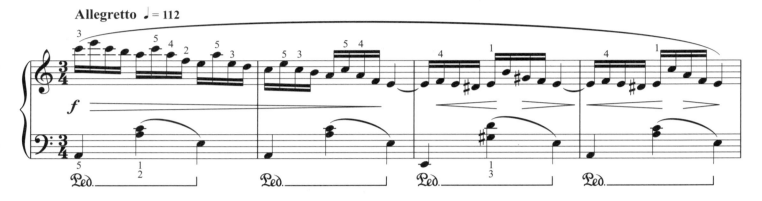

© 2006 Neil A. Kjos Company. From *Schytte: Sixteen recital Etudes* (GP444)
Reprinted with permission 2016. www.kjos.com

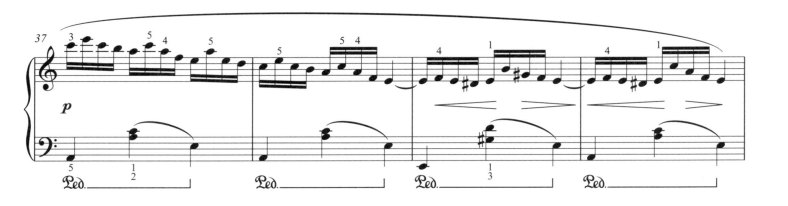

No. 2 from Kinderstücke

op. 72 no. 2

Felix Mendelssohn
(1809-1847)

© Copyright 2017 Trinity College London Press

Fiesta

from *Miniatures*

Joaquín Turina
(1882-1949)

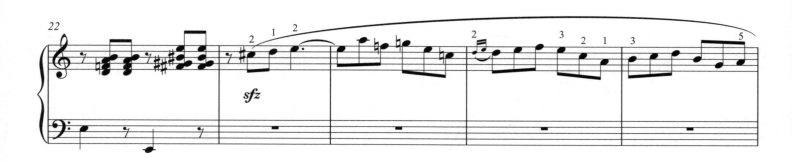

18

© 1930 SCHOTT MUSIC, Mainz © renewed 1958. Reproduced by permission. All rights reserved

[Blank page to facilitate page turns]

Aftermath

Theodore Chanler
(1902–1961)

© 1942 by Theodore Chanler. Reproduced by permission from
Homage to Paderewski (ISMN 979-0-202-52330-8)

Lento

Second movement from *Sonatina*

David Earl
(b. 1951)

© Copyright 2017 Trinity College London Press

[Blank page to facilitate page turns]

Sarah

Thomas Peter-Horas
(b. 1959)

© 2006 C.F. Peters Ltd & Co. KG, Leipzig

Exercises

1a. Obsessive Nature – tone, balance and voicing

Copyright © 2017 Trinity College London Press

1b. Con Amore – tone, balance and voicing

Copyright © 2017 Trinity College London Press

2a. Sunrise – co-ordination

Copyright © 2017 Trinity College London Press

2b. Vamp Style – co-ordination

Copyright © 2017 Trinity College London Press

3a. Top Ten – finger & wrist strength and flexibility

3b. Under Control – finger & wrist strength and flexibility

Copyright © 2017 Trinity College London Press

Teaching notes

Handel — Allegro (from *Suite no. 7 in G minor*, HWV 432) — page 3

George Frideric Handel was born in 1685, the same year as J S Bach and Domenico Scarlatti. A very famous composer in his lifetime, he wrote a number of popular operas, oratorios, and anthems as well as keyboard music. *Allegro* comes from his *Suite no. 7 in G minor* for harpsichord. The movement is in binary form, the first half modulating to the relative major (B♭). The second half passes through two other related keys on the way home (the subdominant in bar 40 and the dominant minor in bar 44), clearly signalled by cadential trills.

When playing Baroque music on the piano it is important to add dynamic variety as well as phrasing and articulation. A solid *f* is a suitable dynamic level for the character at the start, lightening a little in bar 9 and with an echo effect possible in bars 15-16 (there is another similar echo in bars 35-36). A drop to *p* works well for the start of the second half (bar 25), growing to *mp* from bar 29 and then *mf* in bar 33. The return to the home key (bar 45) implies *f*, but within all the suggested dynamic levels it will feel natural to add shaping to the lines with *crescendo-diminuendo* hairpins. Quavers sound best when played lightly detached, but some slurs are possible. A certain amount of overholding in the right hand is stylistically appropriate in places where a melodic line is implied within the figuration. In bars 9 and 10, for example, we might hold on to the first semiquaver of the bar for the length of a crotchet, and the fifth semiquaver to the end of the bar. A brisk tempo is required for performance but a playing at a variety of different speeds in practice is excellent for control and finesse.

Mozart — Minuet in D major, K. 355 — page 6

The *Minuet in D* is a late work featuring daring chromaticism and bold dynamic contrasts. For such a short piece it is full of riches and surprises. The texture is in three parts as though conceived in terms of a string trio (with the occasional octave doubling in the upper part and double stops in the middle part). As is customary in a Classical minuet, the form is binary moving from tonic to dominant at the double bar, then back to the tonic by the end.

The given fingering ensures a *legato* between both parts in the right-hand thirds at the start (bars 1-4); balance the sound slightly in favour of the upper voice and aim for precision in sounding the thirds together. Do not be timid with the *sforzandos* (bar 5, etc) yet allow the tension to release in the *p* bar that follows; the left-hand crotchets can be slightly separated here (bar 6, etc). Relax the mood at the codettas (bar 12-16 and 40-44) and lighten the left hand here by playing the quavers in the middle voice detached. The dissonance is most extreme at the beginning of the second half, the *f* at bar 17 should be pronounced. Maintain the tension in the unison passage between bars 24 and 28, relaxing the tempo slightly in the *diminuendo* at bar 28. Savour the varied setting of the opening theme in bar 29. Discreet use of the pedal will assist with some of the awkward joins and provide warmth and resonance to the sound; take care not to blur the lines or cover over phrase endings.

Eberl — Allegro (1st movt from *Sonate*, op. 6) — page 8

Anton Eberl was a student of Mozart, a famous touring piano virtuoso and a much-admired composer in his day. Nowadays his music is virtually forgotten, however. The *Sonate in C* is clearly inspired by the orchestra, and a vivid performance will bring out the contrasts not only in dynamics but also in the changes of texture and mood and character between the various themes.

Eberl belonged to a period when the composer indicated those notes that were to be played *legato*. It is up to the performer to decide how to play notes that do not have any articulation marks; in a fast movement such as this they are likely to be detached. All notes in the opening *f* phrase should be separated, the last two crotchets crisply so; the left-hand crotchets in bars 8-9, 28, etc, are also detached. Carefully observe all two-, three- and four-note slurs as well as whole-bar phrases (bar 3, etc) by making the last note softer and slightly shorter. Clarity of texture is paramount, so use the pedal sparingly. By all means add a direct pedal to highlight the *fp* in bar 8, and direct pedals to the chords in bar 20, etc. Light touches may be used for warmth and resonance in the *dolce* second theme (from bar 24) and the codettas (bars 43-49 and 89-95). With Baroque and Classical period works in particular, it is good to practise from time to time without any pedal to keep your sound clear and transparent.

Schytte — Etude in A minor, op. 58 no. 6 — page 13

Ludvig Schytte was a Danish composer, pianist and teacher of the late Romantic period whose teachers included Niels Gade and Franz Liszt. *Etude in A minor, op. 58 no. 6* is a study in control of right-hand broken-chordal figurations and scale patterns over a left hand that features jumps. The tempo is fairly brisk (*allegretto*) and the character dance-like. The form is ABA, the contrasting middle section in the relative major key of C.

Aim for evenness in the RH semiquavers, maintaining a *legato* as you shape the phrases according to the dynamic markings and the *crescendo-diminuendo* hairpins. Pay careful attention to the fingering, making sure to stick to it each and every time you practise. Once ingrained you will find you will be able to play without thinking about which note or which finger comes next, enabling you to focus on communicating the musical message in performance. Slow practice is an excellent way to begin learning; return to it on occasion thereafter to keep the fingers in shape. You may also find value in practising the semiquavers in a variety of different rhythmic patterns (try a dotted rhythm, then *slow-quick-quick-quick*, etc). The left hand requires care in measuring the distances accurately and freely, and a certain amount of routine separate-hand practice will guarantee success. Judicious use of the pedal is called for throughout; there are two types of pedalling involved, direct and *legato*. In direct pedalling (A sections) the hand and foot go down and come up together; in *legato* pedalling (B section) the foot goes down just after the hand.

Mendelssohn — No. 2 from Kinderstücke, op. 72 — page 16

Mendelssohn wrote his set of six *Children's Pieces, op. 72* for his young relatives during his summer holiday to England in 1842. No. 2, an *andante sostenuto* in the key of E♭, close in spirit to the composer's many *Songs Without Words*, features a lyrical melody in the right hand supported by gently flowing semiquaver patterns in the left.

After a short introduction based on the tonic and dominant chords the melody appears with the indication *cantabile* (in a singing style). What does this mean for the pianist? Apart from playing the melody more strongly than the accompaniment, we also need to add shaping and shading to the line. Singing it is the very best way to find where the line needs to breathe; you will also discover where the high and low points occur. When you play, aim to replicate the line as though you were singing it. Intervals that are close together are easier to sing (seconds and thirds); those that are further apart may need a little more time to be expressive (give a little more space to the interval of the sixth in bar 9, for example). The left hand needs lightness and delicacy of touch, subtly pointing out the implied bass line (the melodic element in the left hand that underpins the right hand's song) while hiding the repeated notes in between the beats. The left hand, like any good accompanist, needs to accommodate the singing line between phrases as well as helping to move it forwards in moments of intensity (the *crescendo* from bar 14, for example). Beware of interrupting the flow by making a break in sound at phrase ends; a smooth *legato* is called for here.

Turina	Fiesta (from *Miniatures*)	page 18

Fiesta is one of a set of eight pieces entitled *Miniatures* by Spanish composer Joaquín Turina. It makes a very effective recital piece for the intermediate pianist, containing elements of showmanship and display but also calling for imagination and the ability to paint a picture in sound. The Spanish fiesta is an opportunity for people to celebrate by singing, dancing, eating and generally have a good time together in the sunshine, often dressing up in fancy costumes. Researching some images of the fiesta online will certainly put you in the mood to play this piece! *Fiesta* opens with the strumming of a guitar, and soon the dancing starts (bar 11). What is the interruption in bar 15, and what is the singer telling us in bar 23? Is there rain on the way, perhaps? The mood seems to darken here, especially in bars 31–32. Only you can decide what is going on in your story; to help clarify it, you may want to write a paragraph describing it.

The right-hand repeated notes at the start work best with a change of finger on each note as this allows the hand to keep mobile and the arm free. There is some flexibility in the tempo in the right-hand single-line melodies (bars 23–27 and 47–51), otherwise maintain a steady pulse throughout. Careful right-hand practice will help with the awkward chord shapes in bars 11–14 and the descending cascade from bar 39. Beware of over pedalling; short dabs are suitable on each left-hand crotchet from bar 11, etc, and we need to hear the rests in bars 27–28. Whole-bar pedals are effective in bars 45–46 and from 55–58.

Chanler	Aftermath	page 21

Theodore Chanler was an American composer who died in 1961. He is mostly remembered for his songs, but he also wrote an opera, choral music as well as chamber works and music for piano. *Aftermath* was composed in 1942; it is just 21 bars long and has the hallmarks of a song without words in late Romantic style. A successful performance relies on shaping and projecting a melodic line expressively over broken chord patterns, flexibility in timing (*rubato*) and sensitivity to nuance and pedalling.

A two-against-three polyrhythm is featured throughout, with triplets in the left hand and duplets in the right. It is good preliminary practice to master a few scales in this way, in the tempo and style of the piece (remember to start with the hands two octaves apart to avoid a collision). When transferring this skill to the piece approach the triplets with freedom, allowing them to ebb and flow fluidly. As with any piece that has a melodic line, it is always helpful to sing the line first to find out where the breathing places are, and where the high and low point fall. The first note of each of the sighing quaver pairs on the first beats of bars 1–5, etc, is an *appoggiatura* that forms a dissonance with the harmony; play the second note more softly. The climax of the first eight-bar phrase occurs at the highest note, the F♯ (bar 6); the main climax is at bar 13. There is one pedal to each harmony (crotchet beats); longer pedals are required in bar 13 and in the *dolcissimo* (hold the last two beats of the bar in one pedal).

	Lento	
Earl	(2nd movt from *Sonatina*)	page 25

Born in 1951, David Earl is a South African-born pianist and composer resident for many years in the UK. This is the second movement from the *Sonatina*, composed in 2009. The movement is in polyphonic style beginning with three parts but with a fourth making its presence felt from bar 5. It is helpful to think in terms of a string quartet where all the parts are of equal importance within the ensemble. If we voice slightly in favour of the top notes in general it is more because these higher notes are less resonant than the lower notes on the piano, and would be in danger of being overshadowed by them if we played all parts equally. To hear exactly what is happening in the movement, it is helpful to practise each melodic line by itself and then in combination with another; you might also practise omitting one part at a time while playing the others.

Lento tells us to play slowly, giving the music space. Apart from where marked (the rests in bar 2, etc, and commas at the end of bars 16 and 21), avoid a break in sound at the ends of phrases; allow the music to breathe but connect with some pedal. Distinguish between the three levels of soft playing, *pp* (only from bar 26), *p* and *mp*. Pay close attention to the precise lengths of notes. Aim for finger *legato* wherever possible rather than relying on pedal for joins; the pedal is essential for some connections, as well as for warmth and resonance, but beware of covering over rests (the composer has notated these precisely). The movement allows the performer to convey a mood of wistful contemplation. The closing section (from bar 22) might be a touch slower and *lontano*, creating a sense of 'another place, another time'.

Peter-Horas	Sarah	page 25

Thomas Peter-Horas was born in Germany in 1959. His piano style is best described as crossover, because it mixes elements of classical, jazz and pop. *Sarah* is in ternary form (ABA) with the climax occurring in the B section (bar 36). The first A section, marked *p*, features a lyrical melodic line over an arpeggiated accompaniment. When the A section returns (bar 45) we find a countermelody underneath the original melody, forming an alto part.

In order to project the melody line clearly above the left hand in the opening section it is helpful to think in terms of two different dynamic levels, thus left hand *p*, right hand *mp-mf*; longer right-hand notes (the tied Fs in bar 5, etc) will need more tone to sustain across the bar line. Maintaining a *legato* in the left hand throughout each two-bar harmonic unit (bars 5–6, etc) will help with tonal control and rhythmic stability. Pedal according to each new harmony, enjoying the build-up of resonance. The first pedal change need only occur on the downbeat of bar 7, then again in bar 9. Because bar 10 is a new harmony a fresh change is necessary on the downbeat; bars 36–37 need one pedal for the two bars in order to sustain the bass octave. Some careful slow practice with the right hand alone will help security as well as tonal control in the final section. Aim to hold the long notes in the right hand from bar 48 where possible and where comfortable; allow the upper voice to sing above the alto line, which needs to be play softly within the overall *mf* dynamic.

J S Bach	Prelude in G major, BWV 860	*Henle*

The *Prelude in G* comes from the first book of Bach's *Well-Tempered Clavier*, an important collection of 48 preludes and fugues in every key; G major was a happy and peaceful key for Bach. The time signature of $\frac{24}{16}$ is unusual, indicating all semiquavers are triplets and a tempo that is very light and quick. In keeping with this, a light *staccato* (*leggiero*) touch is suitable in the semiquavers, the quavers being generally crisply detached. The quaver pairs in the RH of bars 11–13 should be played as slurs, since these are *appoggiaturas*. There is a line implied by the first note of each semiquaver group (bars 4 and 5, etc), inviting a slight accent.

This Prelude is built on an underlying harmonic progression that determines how we might shape the piece in performance. The spinning semiquaver patterns in bars 1 and 2, for example, outline the progression I–IV–V⁷–I on a tonic pedal (the left hand repeated Gs). It would be worth playing the harmonic outline either in block chords or simply in two voices (bar 4, etc) for the remainder of the piece to reveal the modulations and overall shape. A strong sense of this harmonic structure will assist with a dynamic plan in performance; for example, you will probably feel a *diminuendo* from bar 1 to 2, followed by a hairpin *crescendo-diminuendo* in bar 4 and bar 5. The diminished chord in bar 6 lends itself to a change of dynamic (perhaps *poco forte*), followed by a lightening of energy in the next bar. A *diminuendo* in the descending sequence from bar 11–13 will feel natural; from the low point in bar 14 you might make a gradual *crescendo* to the triumphant end.

Harris	Study	Trinity

Paul Harris' modern take on the traditional study in finger velocity is appealing and inventive. It provides a refreshing alternative to Czerny and Clementi staples, and is really fun to play. Note how this study in C major that veers off into black and white patterns from the first bar, gives both hands an equal workout. Dexterity in the semiquaver passagework and rhythmic precision throughout are basic requirements; no pedal is necessary.

As you practise, aim to identify as many of the tonal centres as you can (for example, the right hand in bar 3 begins with an ascending scale of E major followed by a decorated five-finger position in Bb major). It is fine to play the opening LH quavers with a light detachment and where the semiquavers flow between the hands, observe where these need seamless continuation (eg bars 13 and 15) or contrast (eg bar 6) as the music suggests. Careful control of the final *crescendo* (from bar 16) will help to achieve a sense of elan in the closing bars. If you struggle to play fluently at the required *allegro moderato* tempo, you will find security in practising at a variety of different speeds, starting slowly and always insisting on complete accuracy in notes and fingerings as well as listening for evenness in rhythm at the given dynamic level. Such careful and disciplined work is indispensable for control; many professional pianists find that returning to slow practice even after they have learned the notes helps them maintain a high level of technical command.

Allegro molto (3rd movt from

Haydn	Sonata in C major, Hob. XVI:50)	Henle

This is the last movement of the so-called 'English' Sonata in C, inspired by the powerful and resonant Broadwood pianos Haydn encountered on a visit to London in the 1790s. The music is full of humour and lightness of spirit, requiring a sense of comic timing in the *fermatas*. In bar 10, for example, Haydn takes a wrong turning and has to stop for a while to figure out how to get back on track. He carries on as though nothing happened, but he loses his way again in bar 65 and yet again in bar 69. Enjoy teasing your listeners in these places as they scratch their heads wondering what Haydn is playing at.

The tempo is *allegro molto* (very lively). Haydn has marked those notes he wants played *legato* and *staccato*; unmarked crotchets work best when lightly detached. The grace notes are played on the beat; since the notes they connect to are all short a good solution is to play the grace note and the main note simultaneously, touching in the grace note as lightly as possible. Two-note slurs should be carefully articulated, with a break after the second note. Pay close attention to the dynamics, the contrasts between *f* and *p* are important for the character changes. Instead of bringing the movement to a strong close, Haydn writes a throwaway ending (marked *p*) and we feel the music scampering away.

Dabs of pedal add colour and resonance to the accents (the spread chords in bars 38, 51, etc) but use it sparsely and cautiously elsewhere to preserve clarity of texture and articulation.

Liszt	Klavierstück in E major, R. 60	Bärenreiter

The *Klavierstück (Piano Piece) in E* is the first of 5, written in 1865. While the technical demands may seem simple enough on first glance, this piece requires care with pedalling, control of touch and tone in soft and loud dynamics, and a feeling for timing in a very slow tempo.

Liszt instructs us to put down the *una corda* pedal (left pedal) at the start and to hold it there until just before the climax (*tre corde* in bar 30). While there is no direction to use it again when the A section returns in bar 37, you may do so at your discretion. The effect of the soft pedal is to change the timbre of the sound by muting it; it is still possible to play firmly and even quite strongly with the left foot down (the *crescendo* from bar 27). Carefully observe the long (right) pedal markings in the introduction; the *staccato* dots under the slur here and elsewhere (bars 31 and 33) indicate a certain emphasis, played non-*legato* but held in the pedal. In bars 35-36 make the tiniest of separations between the *portato* quavers (the effect is like sobbing or panting). Release the pedal carefully on the resolutions in the right-hand line (the B in bar 6 and the F♯ in bar 8, etc) to avoid

smudging the melodic line. In the last two bars, each resolution requires a change of pedal (left hand third beat of bar 44; right hand downbeat of bar 45). The piece is punctuated by rests; enjoy these and make the most of them, remembering that silence can be an important expressive ingredient in music.

Allegro (1st movt from

Mozart	Sonata in G major, K. 283)	Henle

This graceful movement in G major makes almost no use of the minor, except for a short interruption to A minor just after the start of the recapitulation in bar 75; bring out the LH *f* (bars 75 and 79) to highlight the element of surprise. The lyrical first subject is gentle and contented; there is a livelier energy in the transition between first and second subjects (bars 16-22) and it would be unnatural not to respond to the rising sequence here by adding a *crescendo*, so by all means do (Mozart does not write all performance directions in the score, leaving much up to the performer). As is common in first movement sonata form, there are several different ideas in the second subject area – aim to bring a new character to each. There is coyness in the phrase from bar 23-26, the mood changing to playfulness and later exuberance as Mozart heads to the double bar. Make the most of the sudden *p* to *f* contrasts (bar 31, 38, etc).

Quavers that do not have phrase markings or slurs are for the most part non-*legato* (except for the LH from bar 80, which need to supply a harmonic carpet for the RH melody). Give semiquavers passages melodic interest by shaping the lines with *crescendo-diminuendo* hairpins. Ornaments come on the beat, the *appoggiaturas* (bar 37, etc) played as semiquavers. Take care with the pedal; short dabs may be appropriate here and there for resonance but all rests should be clear and audible, and textures clear and transparent. Judicious use of finger pedalling (overholding touch) in the *Alberti* figures (bar 1, etc) adds resonance in the LH while preserving clarity in the RH.

Prokofiev	Vision Fugitive no. 10	Boosey

Visions fugitives (Fleeting Visions) is a set of short untitled pieces written between 1915 and 1917 by Russian composer Sergei Prokofiev. No. 10, marked *ridicolosamente* does not have an actual tempo but a moderate speed gives the player the opportunity to bring out the quirky, grotesque humour and manage the fast notes without rushing. Perhaps the opening LH music sounds like a machine, and the RH the braying of a donkey (the accents need to be very strong, almost strident)? There is a ludicrous march that starts in bar 11, interrupted by mocking laughter in bar 15 as though the music was poking fun at someone. This is certainly not a polite piece!

A strictly metronomic approach would adversely affect the character as much as playing with exaggerated *rubato*. The secret lies in knowing how to place certain events to underline their rhythmic effect. The downbeat of bar 17, for example, may be played very slightly late. There is room for your own personality here, and no two players will interpret the piece in the same way. The last two bars work just as well with a subtle *ritardando* as with a slight hurrying forwards. Pedal, if used at all, must never affect the dryness of the *staccato* quaver pattern that permeates the piece from start to finish; all *legato* connections must therefore be achieved by hand. *Sotto* (bar 18) tells us that the right hand should be under the left; *sopra* (bar 19) the right hand is now over the left. Play the roulades in bars 15 and 16 (etc) very lightly with clean articulation. Grace notes are played before the beat.

Rocherolle	La Chapelle	Kjos

This evocative piece by American pianist and composer Eugénie Rocherolle is beautifully written for the piano, making full use of the pedal to build up sonorities from sustained bass notes and rolling harmonies. It is music from the heart, calling for a romantic spirit and the ability to play freely with *rubato* and plenty of feeling. It makes a very effective recital piece and will be popular with players and listeners alike.

The piece is in two halves, each starting *adagio* and gradually picking up the pace from andante to moderato as the texture thickens and the mood becomes more passionate and expansive. A brief coda returns to *tempo primo* and the hymn-like character of the start. The mood is solemn and reverential yet tender in the two *adagio* sections; allow the quaver movement to help move the music forwards in the *andante* (bars 9 and 30) so that it can build to the climaxes in both *moderato* sections (bars 17 and 38) where the tempo is significantly faster and the feeling joyous. The pedal is your ally when used correctly. To avoid blurs and smudges, make sure to lift the pedal all the way to the top in order to clear all traces of the previous harmony before putting it down again; you will need to be especially attentive to your right foot as the textures thicken. At the *moderato* (bars 17 and 38) take a moment on each new bass note (the first quaver of the bar) to make sure you catch it in the pedal. If you do this well you will build an impressive wave of sound that releases at the end of each RH phrase. You will need to change pedal on each crotchet in bars 8 and 29.

Moment Musical no. 6
Schubert (Plaintes d'un Troubadour) *Bärenreiter*

The title translates as *Complaints of a Troubador*, but it is not Schubert's own. The piece was so named when it made its first appearance in an album of short pieces by various composers published in Vienna in 1824; it later became the final piece in Schubert's set of six miniatures, the *Moments musicaux*. The form is ABA, each section itself in ternary form; the *da capo* repeat after the Trio is mandatory in any performance. One of the hallmarks of Schubert's music is his distinctive use of harmony, allowing his music to move through different tonal regions and often touching on unexpected harmonies on the way. When the music changes to the key of E major in bar 29, the mood seems to change with it; is there a bittersweet feeling here, a sense of longing?

The tempo is *allegretto*, so not too fast. A slow minuet tempo allows the necessary space to underline the many moments of harmonic and textural beauty in performance, and while the piece may not look too difficult at first glance it requires a thoughtful approach in the practice room. An important consideration is achieving a good tonal balance at each dynamic level, from $\boldsymbol{pp}$ to $\boldsymbol{ff}$ (notice where the dynamic changes are sudden, and where they are prepared by a *crescendo* or *diminuendo*). Chord voicing is another challenge to overcome, requiring very careful listening and experimentation until you find the right blend from all the notes in the chords (rather than projecting a top melody line). The lower notes in both hands from bar 17-20 contribute more to the soundscape than the repeated C♭ on the top, for example, and moments of contrary motion between the parts need to be heard clearly (bars 4, 22, 35, etc). Breathe between phrases, and create *legato* by hand wherever possible.

Skulte Arietta *Peters*

Ādolfs Skulte was a Latvian composer and music educator who died in 2000. *Arietta (Little Song)* is in neo-Baroque style requiring a projected singing tone in the RH, a full range of dynamics, sensitivity to phrasing and harmony and good control of the pedal. The tempo is slow, the mood solemn and the character noble.

Think of the top line as though sung by a soprano voice, or played on a violin. The first beat of each bar is marked with a *tenuto*, telling us to give the note more weight; shape the line beautifully by emphasising its high and low points and allowing it to breathe naturally at the ends of phrases. To help you project the melody clearly, the LH needs to be quite a bit softer. However, because there is a lot of interest in the LH it is worth practising it by itself on occasion, savouring the dissonant harmonies and bringing out the slurred quavers expressively, as though sighing (bar 6, etc). Resist the temptation to spread the left-hand chords; all notes need to sound precisely together. Observe all dynamic markings carefully; the challenge is not to play so softly in the $\boldsymbol{p}$ at the start that the $\boldsymbol{pp}$ in bar 36 cannot be softer. Similarly with the *fortes* on the first page, keep something in reserve for the $\boldsymbol{ff}$ at the climax in bar 31. *Legato* pedal is essential in this piece; as a general principle, change on each crotchet beat making sure to listen for the RH rests, which are breathing places.

This atmospheric piece comes from Mark Tanner's *Nightscapes for Piano*. It requires responsiveness to the mood, a vivid imagination and careful control of left hand and pedal.

The hands are placed far apart leaving a big gap in the middle of the texture (a main contributing factor to the bleakness of the title), and the LH is much more active than the RH. Listen very carefully to the LH, aiming for a smooth and even effect in the semiquaver patterns while sensing that each half-bar unit creates a wave (shallow waves in the outer sections but bigger ones in the middle section from bar 11). Important bass notes are marked *tenuto*; give these a little more time not only because of the leaps but also because they add a bass dimension that complements the RH's high treble register and the gulf between the hands. Despite the $\boldsymbol{pp}$ marking the RH will need a certain amount of projection and shine to give it profile. Apart from bars 18 and 19, where a long pedal is marked, we change the pedal twice per bar. This type of long pedalling creates mild dissonance from neighbouring notes that are not part of the harmony, but don't be afraid of this build-up of sound – this gentle mistiness is absolutely what we are after here. In the middle section you may be tempted to change the pedal on the second and fourth beats but resist this at all costs; the marked pedalling creates a lovely effect, allowing a build-up of resonance as the mood becomes more fervent.

Teaching notes written by Graham Fitch

Key

A solid line denotes a piece within this book.

A dotted line denotes a piece from the alternative list.